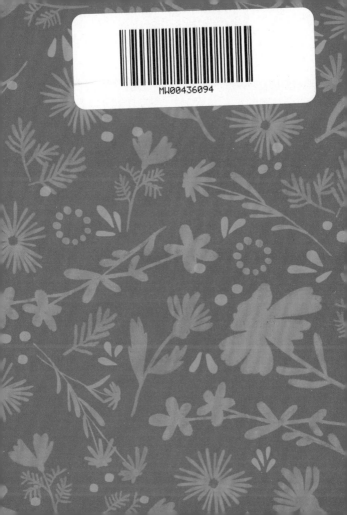

A WHOLE BOOK OF THINGS I LOVE ABOUT MOM

1

You are so incredibly

Selfless ♡ ________________.

2

Your

____

has always amazed me.

3

Because of you, I believe I can

do Anything I put my mind to.

4

I feel so lucky to
have inherited your

long, thin, beautiful

Legs!

6

5

I wish I'd inherited your

beautiful Green eyes

(but glad I got

Dad's baby blues!)

6

I love hearing
your stories about

- growing up in Redding.
- times in HHI
- stories about my
brothers + grownups!

7

I wish I could've
been there when you

________________________________.

8

When I was little,
I loved to watch you

1 be everyone we know
'Home Nurse'
2 - Patient wife
3 - Compassionate Human
(cheering for the other team)

9

If we could go back in time, I'd

Snuggle between you & Dad watching some comedy just the with ~~you~~ 3 of us again.

10

You've always made me feel so

strong, independant,

and LOVED!

11

You didn't freak out when I

~~showed off my ladybug~~ any of my tattoos.

Thank you for that - I know that wasn't easy.

12

You even supported me through my

selfish, bratty, thought I knew everything but really knew NOTHING!

phase.

(Sorry, again.)

13

You put up with my

____

(and love me anyway).

14

I hate to admit it,
but you were right about

pretty much most major decisions!

- Bangs - always right.
- quick purchases
- Doctor Appt's!

15

I don't know what I'd do
without your advice on

1 - Lillian Scarlet Fenner

2 - Anything involving
Anyone I know -
- medically
- emotionally
You! Are my source of truth.

16

You've always
encouraged me to

Do the best I can
with what I know.

17

Your passion for

helping others

inspires me.

follow in your footsteps.

18

You have the most beautiful

Heart

in the world.

19

When I'm feeling

- Sad
- proud
- happy
- scared
- emotional
- ME!

I still crave your

- guidence
- strength
- advice
- love
- approval

20

You are so

- Loved + Respected

- Admired - nurse - mom - sponsor, - Aunt - Grandma - Sister - SIL - Godmoth - Friend

and

______________________.

21

When I was a kid,
I thought you were

a 'Superhero' ________.

nd I still DO! ☺

22

I still think you're

a hero -Family -Friends -Strangers

23

I secretly love it
when you call me

Ja.

24

If I had to describe you
in one word, it would be

Super Grandma

NP

25

You have the best taste in

- Chocolate.
- Hotels
- Cars - boochy ♡
- Snuggle Movies
- Bedroom views: Beach sunsets

26

I love how you taught me
to appreciate

All humans.

27

I'll never get tired of your

hugs, Calls, texts,

Sewing gifts, Choc. Chip Cookies,

All + every home cooked meals,
advice, stories, pictures!

CA

28

I love how you've
never been afraid to

talk to strangers.
& share your goodness.

29

You're the most incredible

-Mom -Wife

Grandmother -Sister

friend -

in the world. - Nurse

+Practioner

Sparser

-Skier

Cowarker

-Baker

-Chef

30

I can only hope to be half as

an amazing social conscious human/mother/grma/sister/friend

as you one day.

I Lo

e YOU,

Mom!

Created, published, and distributed by Em & Friends
11111 Jefferson Blvd. #5167
Culver City, CA 90231
emandfriends.com
Em & Friends is a registered trademark of Knock Knock LLC
Fill in the Love is a registered trademark of Knock Knock LLC

Printed in China

FSC
www.fsc.org
MIX
Paper from responsible sources
FSC™ C008047

ISBN: 9781642445602
UPC: 812729026458

12